GLASS, STONES & CROWN,

The Abbé Suger and the Building of St. Denis

Anne Rockwell

Atheneum   1968   New York

To Rocky

PROLOGUE

From Athens the stranger came to Roman Gaul. He reached the Roman city of Arles, near the Mediterranean Sea and then traced his way ever northward along the banks of swift, dark rivers of inland Gaul, through its deep and lonely forests. Although the wild beasts of the forest howled, and each cracking branch meant possible danger, the stranger must have feared the sound of a human voice as much as any other, for the message that he carried was not welcome in Gaul. The stranger's name was Denis, and he had come to tell the wild and savage tribesmen of Gaul the story of Jesus Christ, who had been dead now more than two hundred years. The Roman rulers of the land felt that this story carried a threat to all the might and power of Imperial Rome and they fought belief in the new religion, by killing if necessary, any Christians they could find.

But still Denis continued his dangerous journey. At last he reached a large Roman settlement called Lutetia. This settlement consisted of an island village in the River Seine with many deep, rich limestone quarries on the surrounding river banks. Here Gallic slaves, driven by Roman soldiers, cut and dragged out huge blocks of creamy stone. With this stone the Romans built temples to their gods and goddesses, homes and baths. But most of all they built their long, endless-seeming roads, leading on always into the next wilderness. It was among these miserable quarry slaves that Denis lived and worked, telling them of Jesus. And many Gauls, and Roman soldiers too, listened to him and began to call themselves Christians.

But the news of what he was doing reached the Roman governor, and Denis was taken prisoner and tortured, along with two faithful followers and friends, Rusticus and Eleutherius. The Romans demanded that they publicly deny the religion they were teaching, but this the three men refused to do. Rusticus and Eleutherius died of the tortures inflicted on them, and Denis was taken to a hill high outside the town and his head was chopped off. Then, legend tells, Denis picked up his decapitated head and singing joyfully made his way down the hill, followed by a band of angels. On and on he wandered, for more than five miles, until at last he reached a certain spot in a wide meadow. Here he lay down and died. A Christian woman named Catulla buried him there, along with his two companions.

The Roman persecution of the Christians went on, but in Gaul, the damage was done. St. Denis (for such he was soon called) had brought a message that spread from person to person, to tribesman and Roman alike. When, at last, more than a hundred years after the death of St. Denis, the Emperor Constantine of Rome himself became a Christian and the long persecutions ended, Christianity was already well established in Gaul.

The centuries passed, and the Romans gradually left Gaul; the colony of Lutetia came to be called Paris, after a Gallic tribe, the Parisii, who lived there. The high hill where St. Denis had been executed was called Montmartre, or the Martyr's Mount. And in the wide meadow where St. Denis and his two companions lay buried, a shrine was built where people came and asked the special blessing of the saint. About the year 630 a king of one of the greatest Gallic tribes, the Franks, placed his throne in this shrine. He planned that all future kings of the Franks would be crowned and buried here, that they might receive the special favor of the saint, for themselves and their people. This king was named Dagobert, and he was chief of many men.

At the same time, he gave the surrounding meadows to a group of monks. They would tend the church, plant vineyards and orchards to support them-

selves, and live and worship there. A few frayed Roman manuscripts in the possession of the monks became the nucleus of a library, to which the monks diligently added stories of the saints, chronicles of the Frankish kings, modern sermons and poems; all were written by hand on parchment and decorated in the margins with playful drawings of miracles, men and demons.

In addition to land, King Dagobert gave the monks the right to hold a fair outside of their monastery. Here farmers and traders and craftsmen could gather to buy and sell each other's wares, and also sell to the pilgrims who visited the shrine at St. Denis. From the rents charged for booths at this fair, the monks received an income that enabled them to take care of the shrine and its holy relics.

About a hundred years after the reign of Dagobert, in 775, when Charlemagne was King of the Franks, a new and larger shrine was built for St. Denis. And over the years, the library at the monastery grew and grew, until its collection of manuscripts was one of the finest in the Western world. Around this library, a little school developed. And it was to this school in the year 1090, that a peasant brought his bright and lively nine-year-old son. The boy was to be instructed in all that the monks could teach him.

At school, the boy quickly made friends with another boy, exactly his age. It was a close friendship, one that was to last for life. The peasant's son was named Suger, and his friend was Louis Capet, son of Philip I, King of the Franks, and next heir to the ancient throne of Dagobert.

CHAPTER ONE

rom the time he started school, Suger amazed his teachers. His answers to questions were clever, and his ideas were intelligent; his speech sparkled with gay puns and plays on words.

He was an eager reader, and thought much about what he read. When he examined the chronicles of past Frankish kings, it worried him that the monarchy of his own time was much weaker than it had been in the great days of Charlemagne, hundreds of years earlier. Charlemagne had rallied his nobles around him and made his kingdom strong and large, so that justice, learning and civilization flourished over a wide area.

Even the mighty caliph who ruled Jerusalem, Harun-al-Rashid, had so feared Charlemagne that he had offered him the keys to Jerusalem and promised that any Christian might come there and worship in safety. Harun-al-Rashid had sent Charlemagne gifts of elephants, jewels, and priceless manuscripts, so much did he wish the good will of the mighty Frankish king. This was a great concession, for the followers of the

Prophet Mohammed, who were called Saracens, had ruled the city of Jerusalem since 638. Though Christians regarded this city as their holiest shrine, under the Mohammedans, they were dependent on the tolerance of individual rulers, called Caliphs, for the privilege of living and worshiping in the holy city. Many caliphs allowed Christians to live in Jerusalem, so long as they paid higher taxes than Mohammedans, and even allowed them to build shrines and churches, so long as they were never as tall as a Mohammedan mosque, but the relationship between the two groups was that of an uneasy peace, which often flared up into fighting and violence.

It was actually during the reign of Charlemagne's grandfather, Charles Martel, that Charlemagne's power over the Saracens had begun. Charles Martel had defeated the Saracen army at the Battle of Poitiers and had saved the Western world from a forced conversion to Mohammedanism. Pepin the Short, Charlemagne's father, and Charlemagne, himself, had maintained this advantage and had extended their power over the Frankish lands, though at the end of Charlemagne's reign Vikings did succeed in coming in at the north. Yet even so, this had been a time of glory and greatness.

At the end of the eleventh century, when Suger was a student, all of this was changed. The King of the

Franks was nearly powerless. Bullied by the very nobles who owed him allegiance, he watched helplessly as these nobles made war on one another, trampling down the fields the peasants planted and burning the towns where merchants and craftsmen lived. Taxes were unpaid; the King was impoverished and alone, with no one he could depend on to help him defend his lands against outsiders.

Worse yet, in 1096, when Suger was fifteen, many people completely deserted their homes and children to follow a wild and passionate monk, Peter the Hermit, on a journey to Jerusalem. They all hoped to free the city from Mohammedan rule and thus save their souls. Instead, when they reached the city, disorganized, undisciplined, ragged and hungry, they were slaughtered helplessly.

As a boy growing up in this confused world, Suger

thought long and hard about these things, for they troubled him. And there was another matter that troubled him. It had to do with the pilgrims who came to St. Denis.

Each spring, when the first crocuses and wild hyacinths poked up through the black earth, men and women tried to shake off the darkness and depression of the long, cold, dreary winter, and they set off on pilgrimages. Throughout Europe, the roads were soon dotted with pilgrims headed for the church of some famous saint where they might see the relics, bones or possessions believed to have belonged to the saint, encased in coverings of gold and jewels. The pilgrimage itself and sight of these relics, embellished by all of an artist's skill, brought beauty and glamour to many otherwise drab lives. Stories were told, games were played, and songs were sung along the pilgrimage routes. A pilgrimage was a chance to rid oneself of boredom and despair, to see the world, to make new acquaintances, and perhaps to find peace for a troubled soul.

Throughout the summer and into the last warm days of autumn the pilgrims wandered, stopping at this minor shrine or that along the way, until they reached the destination they had chosen. In early October the great annual fair of St. Denis was held, Dagobert's fair,

which by Suger's time had grown to monumental size. Here Saxon merchants brought wool and furs from their Northern homes to sell to the Frankish merchants, and bought wine and honey to store up for the long winter ahead. On October 9, the religious feast of St. Denis was held, and the merchants found many customers in the pilgrims who had gathered to visit the church.

Suger witnessed this feast for many years. And to him, it was an alarming sight. Hordes of eager pilgrims swarmed into the mouldy, small, dim church. Eager to see the sights that had brought them so far, people forced their way forward, shoving and pushing into space that was not there. For the church had become too small. At times Suger watched with alarm, knowing how easily the ancient walls, rent now with deep cracks, could collapse under the pressure of bodies pressing against them. Women climbed, screaming and sobbing hysterically, onto the shoulders of the men . . . . emotions ran wild . . . . and many people were carried out, fainted dead away.

To Suger, it seemed that this church, home of the Apostle of the Gauls and patron saint of the Frankish Kings, was unworthy of its high place. He began to dream of a shrine more beautiful than any he had ever seen.

The two boys grew into men, and in 1108 Louis was crowned Louis VI, King of the Franks. His lands were small; his powers were few; his treasury was poor; but he and Suger, who was now secretary to the Abbot Adam of St. Denis, talked of a new, strong kingdom, a kingdom like Charlemagne's.

As a first step, because of Suger's tact, sense of justice, and ability to see two sides of a question, Louis VI, in 1121, appointed him Ambassador to the Pope at Rome. A bad relationship with the Pope had developed under Louis' father, Philip I, and Suger's job was to mend the breach.

Suger went immediately to the ancient, ruined city of the Roman Emperors, and there he lived and worked for more than a year. His mission was a success; the Pope listened to the King's plea and made peace; and in 1122 Suger, his job done, began the long journey back to Paris.

On his way back, he was overtaken by a messenger from St. Denis. The Abbot Adam, he was told, lay dead. The monks had held an election to choose a new leader, and their choice was Suger.

CHAPTER TWO

So it was as Abbot of St. Denis that Suger returned home. He knew at once that with his new power he intended to do two things. He was going to increase the power of the King of the Franks and, at the same time, glorify and enlarge the church of St. Denis.

It was the church that mattered most to him, but the King came first. Little by little, bit by bit, victory by victory, the King, with Suger's close guidance, put down the nobles who were persecuting the people and made peace with the Kings around him. Yet, something more than this was needed. The nobles had to be united by one cause, for there was no nation, as we know it today, to inspire loyalty and create unity. Instead, there were many nobles controlling the land, often with conflicting ambitions, and each with a vague and poorly defined allegiance to the king.

Suger thought he knew how to overcome this. The knights and noblemen, burghers and peasants all showed intense devotion to the patron saint of the

Franks, St. Denis. Why couldn't this loyalty and love be transferred to the office of the King, if the King were to proclaim himself not merely a somewhat more important feudal noble, but the earthly vassal and representative of St. Denis.

In 1124, shortly after he had become abbot, Suger had a chance to test this idea. Henry V, Emperor of Germany, was about to invade the Frankish lands. His army was large; his knights were brave and well-disciplined. Should Louis be unable to control his unruly nobles, disaster and defeat awaited him.

The army came, the battle lines were drawn, and the battle was to begin. At this moment Louis left his assembled army and went into the church of St. Denis to receive, from Abbot Suger, the ancient banner of golden flames on red silk that had always been the symbol of St. Denis. This banner was called the "Oriflamme." Louis rode before his army carrying this banner, and behind him flocked many more nobles than Louis had believed would ever follow him to battle. They were, it seems, willing to fight to the death, not for the King, but for St. Denis. When Henry V saw the mighty army led by the King of the Franks, he retreated without even drawing his sword. And as he left he could hear only the roaring cry of the Frankish nobles, chanting, "Montjoie, St. Denis!"

It had worked, and it was to work again and again. For more than three hundred years no King of the Franks went to war without carrying the precious Oriflamme, summoning all the loyalty this banner could call forth. It could unite the King, his feudal nobles, and the people, when all else failed. A beginning had been made; a nation was being built, a nation that would call itself France.

With a beginning made on one great problem, Suger began work on the other. From the beginning of his abbacy, he had put aside large sums of money for the repair of the church. Now, from near and far he assembled goldsmiths, painters, and carpenters to repair the parts of the church that were most crumbled. But he was not satisfied with this. What he really wanted to do was tear down the old church and build a new one.

In the abbey, the monks were much opposed to this idea. The church was so old and so filled with history and legend that, to them, the very stones seemed holy. There was even a legend that Christ Himself had appeared at the consecration of the building, long, long before. There was another story of how, when the church was just being completed, the master-builder, a monk named Airard, had climbed up to the bell-tower to remove the last scaffolding. Sud-

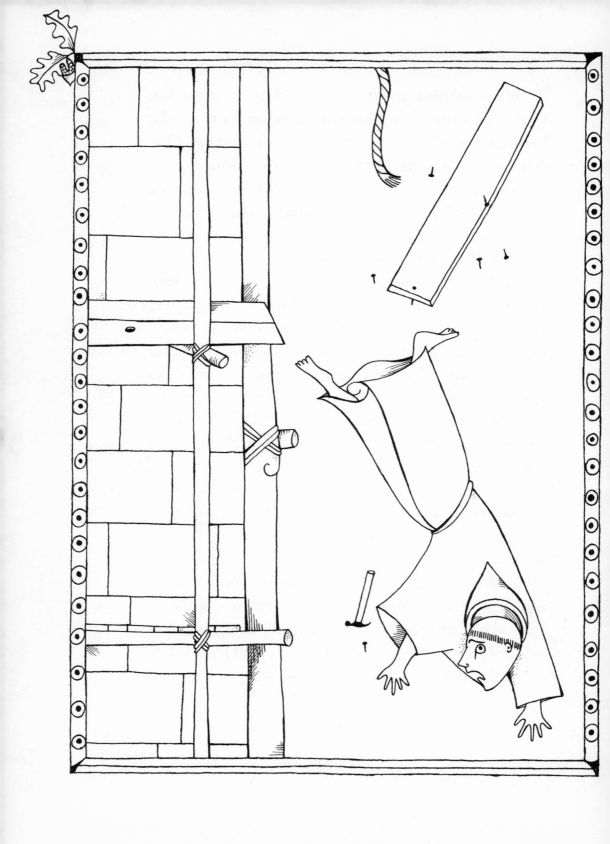

denly he was hit by a plank falling from above, and he had tumbled headlong through the air. But then, miraculously, so it was written in the old records of the abbey, he had stood up and walked, saved, it was believed, by the mercy of St. Denis. All the monks took this as a sign that their church was pleasing to the Saint.

With such miracles as these embodied in the stones of the church, what might happen, wondered the monks, to the man who dared disturb them? In this, as in all things, Suger was prudent and diplomatic. For a while he contented himself with repairing those parts that were most dilapidated. But he optimistically continued to save large sums of money from the annual fair and, at the same time, asked wealthy pilgrims to donate their jewels toward the rebuilding of the church.

In the meantime, by placing a mural here and there, wherever the masonry was in need of patching up, the church was made to look as fine as possible. But it was still too small. Suger dreamed of a temple that would rival Solomon's in its magnificence. Or perhaps even the jeweled mosques of the Mohammedans. He had heard pilgrims who had visited Jerusalem tell of these great, glowing structures. If he could find out how to do it, his building would be as grand.

But other things demanded the Abbot's attention.

Louis had grown ill. He had become so obese that even breathing had sometimes become difficult for him. He is still remembered by his nickname, Louis the Fat. Furthermore, he suffered from a trembling sickness that grew progressively worse. Many around him believed that his poor health was the result of an attempt made by his stepmother, many years earlier, to poison him. To make matters worse, in about 1130 his eldest son, a brave knight named Philip, was out riding when his horse awakened a pig that was sleeping along the muddy banks of the Seine. In a panic the pig ran, squealing shrilly, in front of the horse and tripped him, throwing young Philip to the ground. The prince was carried home, dead before he arrived.

From the school at St. Denis, Louis fetched his second son, a ten-year-old boy who was also called Louis. This boy's one ambition had always been to be a cloistered monk. Now, however, his wishes were left behind. He had no choice but to be trained in the ways of court and knight, that he might one day become King. But although Suger and the King tried their best to change the boy into a feudal courtier, he pined for the peaceful life of a monk and both his father and Suger worried about him.

And all the while Louis VI grew increasingly fatter, until finally he was so fat that he could not even mount his horse unaided. It was at a time when both Louis and Suger despaired of the future of France that a wonderful opportunity presented itself. In 1137, young Louis was seventeen, and his father was able to arrange a marriage for him with Eleanor, the fifteen-year-old daughter of the Duke of Acquitaine. She would one day rule over vast, rich lands to the south of Paris, lands that stretched from the English Channel to the Mediterranean Sea, and touched the Spanish border. These lands were more extensive than those ruled over by Louis himself. Furthermore, the girl was beautiful, it was said, intelligent, worldly and sophisticated. It was a marvelous match and one that would greatly increase the domains of the King of the Franks. Too ill to travel himself, Louis sent Suger to accompany his son when he met his bride and to see to all the many details of the wedding.

After many papers and treaties had been signed, a glorious wedding was held at Bordeaux. But neither

the father of the bride nor of the groom was present. Just before the ceremony, Eleanor's father had been murdered by one of his own barons, making her Duchess of Acquitaine. Louis VI lay suffering from the summer heat at his country hunting palace just outside of Paris.

In grand style, to the beating of tambour drums and the chanting of crowds, the wedding party started off on the long journey to Paris. Eleanor and Louis stopped many times along the way to visit those nobles who, now that her father was dead, owed their allegiance to Eleanor. The young prince seemed very much in love with his gay and beautiful bride and appeared lively and cheerful in her company. Perhaps, thought Suger, under the influence of this girl, so fit to be a queen, Louis might become less withdrawn and monkish.

He needed to, for along the way to Paris, just as they reached Eleanor's home city of Poitiers, messengers reached them carrying grave news. The King was dead!

And so, the prince and his duchess bride came home to Paris as King and Queen of France . . . . a France that now, with the addition of Eleanor's lands, was larger than it had been at any time since the days of Charlemagne.

CHAPTER THREE

hether the coronation of the new King had any part in it or not, no one can say, but it was in the year that Louis VII became King that Suger finally made the decision to tear down and rebuild the ancient church of St. Denis. Some said that Suger now had time to supervise the building since Louis wished to rid himself of his father's counselor and rule in his own style; but no one knows. Perhaps the death of his childhood friend had simply reminded Suger that life is short, and he felt unable to put off any longer the thing he had hoped all of his life to do.

Putting aside for once and for all the fears of the monks, he assembled masons and carpenters, goldsmiths, sculptors, and glass-makers from all over the land. First he intended to tear down the front end of the church and extend the length of the long part of the church where the worshippers stood, the nave. By lengthening the nave, the church would accommodate many more persons on feast days.

The front of the church had been built in Charlemagne's time. It had a small, dim, tunnel-like entrance, flanked on either side by two squat and dangerously crumbling towers. In place of these Suger and his master-masons proceeded to construct two tall and noble towers. In place of the single tunnel door, they built three majestic bronze doors, representing the three persons of the Trinity. For Suger had decided that nothing in his church would be built that did not express an idea. Over each door was a large, semi-circular arch, and in the stone space between the arch and the door itself, marvelous statues were carved, telling stories of salvation and damnation. Included were carvings for every month of the year, with the activities of men in each season. In one corner there was a figure of Suger himself, put there in hopes that he might be remembered as the man who built the church.

But the most remarkable part of this front was an enormous, circular window of stained glass, placed high above the center door. It was shaped like a rose, and it allowed a wonderful crimson and sapphire colored light to flood the dim interior of the old nave. Although the art of making small objects, such as jewels and cases for relics, of stained glass was one peculiar to the Franks and went far back in time, seldom had stained glass been used in windows. Churches were always dim and dark; though windows pierced the massive stone

walls, here and there, they were generally void of deco-
ration. And often they were just oiled parchment
stretched across a wooden frame. These windows let in
only a dim, dull light, and even they were shuttered
when the church was not in use. So the new window
was something very special, indeed.

As the work progressed, Suger seemed to forget
everything else. His church was all-important because
it was to encompass all he had thought about, all his
life. It was not an easy task. There were many practical
problems that he had to cope with.

In extending the nave, a large number of tall stone columns were needed. These would separate the nave from the side aisles and support the roof vaulting. But wherever Suger inquired, at all the quarries around Paris, no such columns were available, for no place had stone of sufficient hardness and size. Suger refused to let this discourage him. He remembered that many years earlier in Rome he had seen marble columns, finer and taller than any he had seen since, standing in the ruined baths of the Emperor Diocletian. In his mind he began to plan an elaborate scheme for transporting these columns to St. Denis. First they would be taken by barge down a river from Rome to the Mediterranean Sea. Then they would travel over the Mediterranean by ship around the tip of Spain, and up through the English Channel to the mouth of one of the many winding rivers of France. From there they would be brought by barge to the construction site at St. Denis. Needless to say this would require money and organization, not to mention the co-operation of friends and allies abroad. And not only friends and allies must be asked to help, but also the Saracens in Spain, still bitter enemies. But Suger was a skilled and patient diplomat; he felt sure he could find a way to win the help of the Saracens. For St. Denis, nothing was impossible!

Fortunately, this grand scheme for transporting the columns of Diocletian never came to pass. The first of many wonderful bits of luck that contributed to the building of St. Denis made this unnecessary.

About fourteen miles from St. Denis, at the village of Pontoise, stood an ancient quarry. Here, for longer than anyone could remember, workers had carved out millstones used for grinding flour. Suddenly, however, Suger heard that, deep within the quarry, a whole new section had been discovered, where there was much stone of perfect quality and hardness.

Suger and his masons hurried to the spot. The report was true. Here was an ample supply of stone of both the quality and dimension to serve his purpose. When the first stones were quarried and carved roughly into shape for sections of columns, men, women and children — nobles, burghers and peasants alike — hitched themselves, as though they were oxen, to great ropes fastened to the huge stones, lying at the bottom of the quarry. Slowly and triumphantly the people dragged up the mighty stones from the earth.

In this way ordinary people and unskilled people of all kinds were able to help in the building of the church. No doubt the same spirit that sent people off on long pilgrimages over dangerous highways also demanded that they give of their labor in building a

church. It was undoubtedly their hope that, by this pious act, they might help to save their souls. But they were not the only ones involved in the building. Far from it. For there were also men who developed remarkable skill in the dressing and carving of stone and the mathematical skill required to plan such a church. We know little of these men. Although the earlier church had, very likely, been built entirely by monks, it is believed that the men who worked with Suger were laymen. Their knowledge of masonry began in the quarry. Here the rough blocking out of the stone took place. Then, those who in the quarry showed the most skill at carving were allowed to learn work on free-stone, that is, stone already quarried and standing free. This carving took place at the actual construction site, and the freemasons were men of far more precision and accuracy in their carving than the workers in the quarry. Because they traveled from one building site to another, working under various masters, they learned many more carving methods than they might have by staying in one place.

The most skilled and intelligent of the masons learned to use the square and compass. With these two instruments many secrets of geometric proportion were discovered and then realized in stone. This lore, which was passed from one generation to the next, was highly guarded and not written down. For this reason, most of it is lost to us today. But that it was a remarkable body of knowledge is apparent when one knows what these stone-masons built.

Work progressed rapidly on the front. But suddenly Suger directed the masons to stop work on it, although it was not yet complete. He wanted them to begin work on the apse end of the church. This was where the altar was placed, and it was also where the crypt lay. The crypt was an underground chamber where the precious relics of the saints were kept; for they were displayed on the altar only on feast days. The apse was the most sacred part of the church, and when Suger began work on it, it was a small, gloomy, area. Why he began work on the apse so suddenly is not known, but perhaps he had met and hired a master builder of such great talent that the work suddenly became possible, as it had not been before.

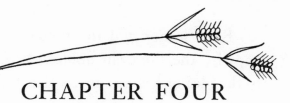

CHAPTER FOUR

t one point during the building of the church, Suger had to leave and go to Poitiers. There was serious trouble there.

When Louis VII had married Eleanor he had inherited the problems of her lands. And one of these had come to a head. The townspeople of Poitiers wished to form a commune; they wanted to band together in time of need and be governed by a mayor of their own choosing. Throughout France at this time, such communes were appearing with considerable regularity. Suger and the former King, Louis the Fat, had always been sympathetic to them. Suger had never lost sight of his own peasant origins; and even in his powerful position as Abbot of St. Denis, he felt sympathy for those who had no power. Furthermore, being a shrewd and sensible man, he saw that if the King aided these communes he would have a powerful ally in the craftsmen and shopkeepers who were a part of them. One day, he might find such good will very valuable, and be able to turn it against nobles who disobeyed him.

But Eleanor and the young King, urged on perhaps by the Poitevan nobles, were violently opposed to the idea of a commune. What right, they asked, had these people to govern themselves? And so, without mercy, Louis VII gathered together all of the people who had joined the commune, along with their children and grandchildren. In the town square, where the people had come, he read a proclamation sentencing all of them to perpetual banishment. Never again could they, or their descendents, live or work in Poitiers. Henceforth, they must wander from place to place, beggars wanted by no one. In the tightly organized society of the Middle Ages, where each man had his place and no other was open to him, banishment was almost worse than death.

Suger, when he heard of this, could not let it happen. He hastened to Poitiers. When he approached the city, he was greeted by a terrible sight. Outside, along the road, lay many prostrate, sobbing people. They were the banished ones. They begged Suger to use his influence to plead for mercy with the King. Suger promised to do so, but it was no easy task. The King was furious and stubborn. Suger argued with all the skill he had that these people had no voice but that of the King, and that he was put there to protect rather than persecute them. At last the King agreed to recall the order of mass banishment.

Although Suger had, with difficulty, prevented Louis from doing one cruel and foolish thing, he was not always so fortunate. The young King, unlike his astute and patient father, found decisions and statesmanship difficult. Under pressure to act, he could behave with impulsive and frightening cruelty.

But, for the most part, there was nothing Suger could do. He returned to his construction work at St. Denis. Each day, each week, each month, he became more and more absorbed in it, and the work proceeded with unbelievable speed. The master-mason at work on the project was an expert at the new art of building with a pointed arch, and the new apse was to be based upon this revolutionary construction device.

Construction by means of arches is a system whereby the great weight of the stones is distributed downward, and the stones bear each other up to prevent their collapsing. To make such an arch, a series of wedge-shaped stone blocks called *voussoirs* are carved. The top of each voussoir is cut wider than the bottom; consequently as they are put in place, one stone above the other, they lock tight together and the weight is passed downward from stone to stone.

Until shortly before the time Suger began work on his apse, an arch usually formed a semi-circle, the

lower side of which was called the *intrados*. Actually, so long as it is constructed of voussoir blocks, an arch can have any shape intrados from flat to severely pointed to horseshoe shaped. But each form of the arch has different characteristics. The nearer an arch is to flat, the greater the outward, or *lateral* pressure on the walls holding it; the more pointed an arch becomes, the less lateral pressure there is. For this reason, an arch forming a semi-circle, which was the kind of arch the Romans had built, while very strong, required walls of tremendous thickness to rest upon.

But the pointed arch was different. It passed its weight directly downward and could therefore rest on much thinner walls, walls that were reinforced by thick stone *buttresses* only at points of stress. Where the pointed arch was first invented no one knows for certain, but it seems to have come from the Arabs. Its first appearance in Europe was on the island of Sicily, after it had been conquered by the Saracen Arabs. The Normans then came and conquered the Saracens, forming the Norman Kingdom of Sicily. From the Saracens, the Normans learned the art of building with the pointed arch. Perhaps they even brought Arab master

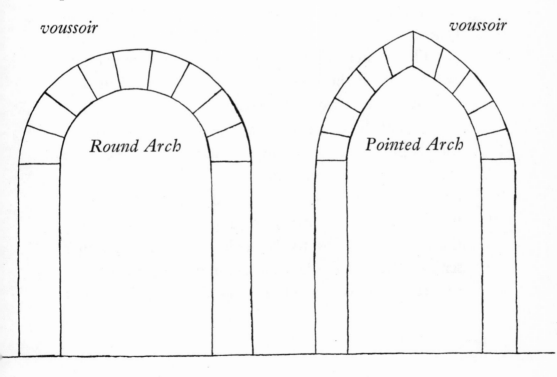

voussoir   *voussoir*

Round Arch   *Pointed Arch*

builders, kidnapped from their Southern land, to help build the tall, fortress-like churches, flanked on either side by extremely tall towers, that soon appeared in Normandy. In many places these churches used the pointed arch.

However, in Normandy the churches were still built with thick walls, lit dimly by tiny, high windows.

While Louis the Fat was King, Suger had acted as peacemaker between Louis and the King of England and Normandy, Henry I, son of William the Conqueror. In the time spent in Normandy talking with Henry, Suger may have noted and admired the churches he saw. It may have been his memory of those structures that formed the basis for his plans for St. Denis.

The master-builder who worked with Suger saw possibilities in the pointed arch that no one had seen before, and he used it in striking new ways. The outside wall of the apse formed a large semi-circle. Within this large curve, nine little spaces for altars were formed as the wall curved further into small semi-circles. At the junction of each of these little curved walls, there was a buttress to support the walls. Inside the apse, a row of twelve columns formed another semi-circle, and inside these columns, another row of twelve columns, set closer together than the first

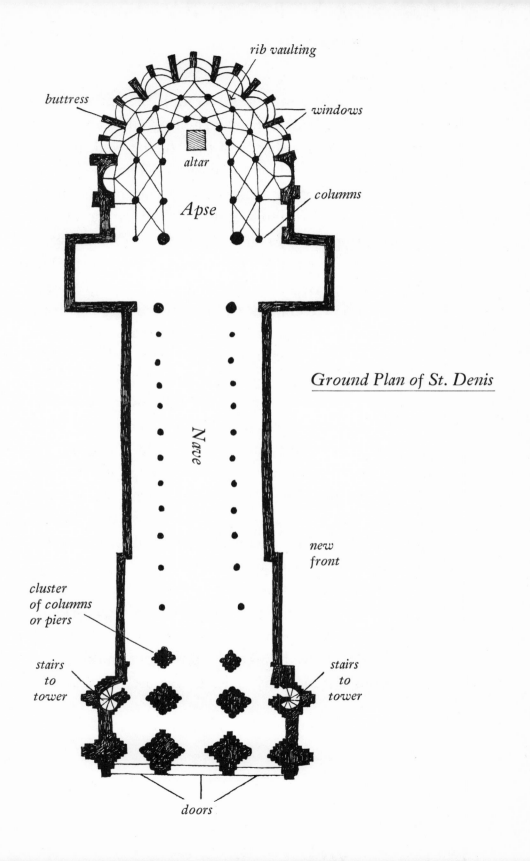

rib vaulting

buttress

windows

altar

Apse

columns

Ground Plan of St. Denis

Nave

new front

cluster of columns or piers

stairs to tower

stairs to tower

doors

formed another semi-circle. Within the space of this final row of columns, the main altar would stand. From one column to another, and then to the wall, pointed arches spanned the overhead space. The roof vaults above them were formed, not of a continuous, heavy row of arches, forming a tunnel, but rather of thin arches springing from one column to another and criss-crossing in the air like a giant, stone, spider web. This system, called *rib vaulting*, has great advantages and it too was a new technique. The criss-crossing ribs form a framework that can later be filled in with lightweight brick and mortar, or small stones, thus lightening the pressure on the outer walls even more. Also, a rib vault requires far less timber for the framework that supports the arches during construction than other kinds of vaulting, for only the spanning arches, and not the connecting membrane walls, require support. But, beyond these practical considerations, a rib vault forms a ceiling that appears to rhythmically rise and fall, like waves in the sea, giving a mysterious look of movement and lightness to inert and solid stone.

The tall, light, thin walls formed in the apse of St. Denis were used at last as nothing more than a framework for the most glorious feature of the church. The ancient art of the Franks, the setting of multicolored bits of glass into strips of lead, was used in windows

that climbed up to nearly the full height of the apse. In ruby red and sapphire glass, stories from the Bible gleamed and lit the apse with a light that was like nothing that had ever been seen.

To Suger and many other thinkers of his time, light itself was divine. Literally they sought from brilliance and light the *enlightenment* and *illumination* that would light and brighten men's minds. Furthermore, to them, light was the least material substance on earth, and therefore closer to the world of pure spirit. To people of that time, the physical building of the church was a very real representation of Heaven itself, though all things on earth were but imperfect shadows of heavenly perfection. What better way, Suger reasoned, to see the things that really mattered, than to have them bathed in a light that seemed to come from Heaven itself.

It is not easy to understand the rich and complicated symbolism of the 12th century. But to the people of the time, it had deep meaning. In Suger's church, there was nothing that did not have, for him and for other people, a clear purpose. And to make sure that no one missed the point, the storytelling windows were further clarified by poems Suger wrote, telling people what to look for in them. It was not only the pictures, however, but the very size and proportions of the walls, the relationship of one part of the building to another, that were determined by the symbolic roles they were to play. For example, the shape of the ground plan of the church itself was like a cross; the cornerstone represented Christ; there were twelve columns in each row in the apse standing for the Twelve Apostles; and the doors entering the church were three, for the three persons of the Trinity. There was much more symbolism, some of which we can only guess at today. Even the soaring arches, carrying the eye upward, were designed to carry the thoughts and the soul upward at the same time.

As he built, Suger was easily able to convince himself that his efforts were pleasing to Heaven. He made much of miracles that seemed to have happened, not to convince himself that his church was good, probably, but to further convince those monks who had been skeptical of the rebuilding. Some of them muttered

away to one another that Suger had, no doubt, melted down the treasured altar jewels in order to create windows of such bright ruby and sapphire. Such was not the case. The windows were made by heating fine river sand, wood ash, and charcoal together until they melted and turned into glass. Oxides of various metals were added to the sand and ash to color the glass. Cobalt added to the mixture made blue, copper made red, manganese made both purple and green, depending upon how long the mixture was heated, and iron made a yellow as bright as gold. Pieces of the colored glass were cut with a red hot poker into any shape desired, and set into curved strips of melted lead, which formed the strong black lines of the drawing. When the lead hardened, the glass was securely fastened. Details of faces and figures were drawn on the glass with a mixture of tiny particles of black iron dust and sticky resin from a pine tree. The process was almost as wonderful and mysterious as if real jewels *had* been used, but to silence his critics, Suger merrily told everyone again and again of the wonderful miracles that had been granted him, both by and for St. Denis.

CHAPTER FIVE

The miraculous story that Suger most enjoyed telling was this: When the time came to vault over the columns from Pontoise, which had been used to lengthen the nave and connect it with the new front, it was necessary to wedge huge timbers between the columns to brace them while the arches spanning them were being built. But in all the forests of that area the tallest trees had been felled many years earlier in order to build defensive walls around castles and towns, during the wars that had taken place. The second growth of trees would not reach the size needed for the stay-braces for years and years. Yet, without such timbers, the church could not be finished. The problem seemed to have no solution, for even if a forest were found many miles away that did have such trees, the cost to buy and transport them would be too great. In those days of many wars, nothing was quite so valuable as a tree, which provided wood for weapons and defenses of all sorts.

Night after night, Suger lay awake wondering

what he should do. At last, one night he was unable to sleep at all. Just before dawn, he rose and awakened the carpenters who were to build the braces. Out through the abbey gates they passed, through the outlying vineyards, fields and pastures, and into the forest . . . all before the sun was up.

Wolves stalked in hunger through the forest in those days, and it was generally only the wood chopper with his strong axe who dared to enter. But the little band of carpenters, pushed on by Suger, crept through the dark forest until, at last, it began to grow light. Then they met a group of wood choppers setting out for their day's work. Suger implored them to tell him the truth — were there *really* no trees of the size he needed in the forest? The men answered that there were certainly none, and all of them knew the forest well. They suggested that Suger and the carpenters return to the warmth and safety of the abbey. Instead Suger insisted that he would find the trees he needed. The wood choppers smiled, and Suger knew they would have laughed out loud if he had not been a person of great importance; but nevertheless he started off with the carpenters again on his search.

Deeper into the forest they went. Then, although not one of them could believe what he saw, they found a tree of a height and a thickness greater than they re-

quired! Before noon, the full number of tall trees had been found, and the work could now go on.

Such a story undoubtedly made an impression on the Abbot's listeners. But this was not all. There was yet another story:

One evening, as the monks were attending service in the church, a violent storm came up. Suger watched with horror as the stone rib-arches, still not stabilized with their vaulting, swayed back and forth, while the wooden roof covering them clattered and banged. All of the monks were terrified, afraid the arches would collapse. If this happened, not only would they perhaps be injured or killed by the falling stones, but the work of many men, over a period of more than a year, would be destroyed in any instant.

The wind blew on until it seemed as though the fragile arches and their swaying columns could bear no more. Then suddenly, the storm stopped. Not a stone had fallen, not one was even loose! The next day Suger learned of the damage done elsewhere by the storm. Strong castle towers lay crumbled to the ground; tall oaks had been ripped out by their roots. The wind had left terrible devastation in the soundest of buildings, yet the precariously balanced stones of the unfinished St. Denis held as if the wind had never touched them. To Suger, and others, this was a sure sign that the

church of St. Denis had received the full protection of Heaven and must therefore be pleasing to God.

As the church grew, so Suger's delight in it grew. He enthusiastically cornered every traveler he met who had ever seen Jerusalem.

"Tell me, tell me," he would ask, "even in Jerusalem, are there such wonders as St. Denis? Is there any shrine more beautiful?"

And even though he was accustomed, as diplomat and politician, to hide his feelings, he could not hide his disappointment when a traveler thought that perhaps, in the wondrous city of Jerusalem, there was such beauty. But few made such an answer, for, to tell the

49

truth, others seemed to be as impressed by Suger's glistening, light-struck marvel, as he was proud of it.

Meanwhile, the years passed quickly and as the Abbot's church came nearer completion, the young King's problems grew greater and his ability to solve them lessened. By 1142 he was involved in a bitter quarrel with his most powerful vassal, Thibault, Count of Champagne. The support of Thibault was vital to France and many times Suger had sought his friendship for Louis the Fat. But young Louis, angered by Thibault, and without consulting anyone, went to war against him. He seized lands belonging to the Count and rushed further and further into brutal battles

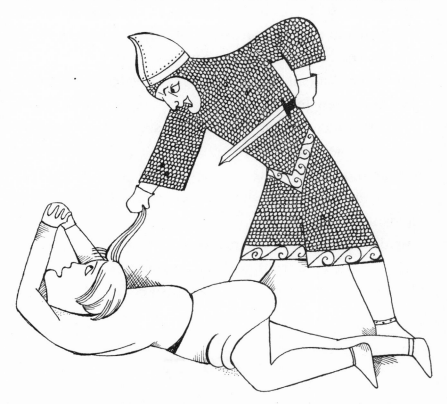

whose end no one could see. France, still barely a nation, was torn apart by civil war. Yet, nothing could stop Louis, though Thibault wanted peace, and what Louis hoped to gain by the war was clear to no one.

One day Louis led his army into the town of Vitry, on the River Marne. The town was made up of craftsmen and shopkeepers and was not defended well by these peaceful and unarmed people. Louis and his men swept through the town, setting torches to all of the thatched roofs and timbered houses, which were set close together on narrow streets. The people of Vitry ran to their church for safety. But the church had a wooden rather than a stone vaulted roof, and the fire did not spare it. The blazing roof fell in; more than a thousand people — men, women, and children — were trapped and burned to death.

Louis collapsed. He could not sleep, for the screams of the people of Vitry awakened him. He became physically ill, weighed down by the horror and guilt he felt over this dreadful thing he had done. All those who were close to him believed that he would die.

The Abbot Suger had for five years remained somewhat aloof from the King and the workings of government. But now he came back to his early work and began to try and bring peace. He began to negotiate between the King and Thibault.

By 1144 the new front and apse of St. Denis were complete. The church could now be consecrated, and Suger planned the consecration ceremony with great care, for it would do more than dedicate a fine church. It would be the occasion to obtain and seal a treaty of peace between Thibault and Louis — a peace that, guided by the patron saint of France, would be, he hoped, a good and lasting one.

o people of the 12th Century, the distance from the natural world to the supernatural was short, and such things as the worship of relics was very real to them. At the village of Chartres, not far from Paris, for example, there was in the church a piece of cloth believed to have been worn by the Virgin Mary. In 911 the Vikings rode down on the village and the people of the town awaited them with terror. But just as the Vikings were ready to force their way through the village gates, the Bishop of Chartres carried the holy relic out and held it up for the Vikings to see. At sight of this relic, so filled for them with mystery and awe, the Vikings grew afraid and fled in a panic. Such feeling was similar to the power Suger had given Louis the Fat when he presented him with the Oriflamme of St. Denis to carry into battle. It was with good reason then that Suger believed his consecration ceremony, as he planned it, would truly bring peace.

When the time came to bless the stones in the new parts of the church, the King, now meek and humble,

53

led the monks in the ceremony. Into the crypt he went, where, from Suger, he received the bones of St. Denis and his companions, encased in jeweled reliquary cases. From the crypt he carried them, before the eyes of Thibault and all his other vassals, to place them on the great jeweled and golden altar of the apse. Here they would remain, brilliantly illumined by the light from the tall stained glass windows, in full view of everyone. After this ceremony, the King of France once again proclaimed himself the vassal of St. Denis, specially chosen to rule the land of this saint. And in this atmosphere, cloaked in ritual and mystery, Suger read aloud the peace treaty he had drawn up. It required that Louis return to Thibault all of the lands he had annexed and cease all war against the Count. For his part, Thibault was to give a splendid gift of rubies and other precious stones to the treasure of St. Denis, in thanks for the part the church had played in bringing peace to his land. Louis and Thibault swore friendship and loyalty on the relics, and the peace was sealed. It was a time of great rejoicing for all the people, for to them the war had seemed endless.

But for Louis VII this was not enough. The peace obtained for him could not erase his guilt over the murders he had committed. Even his queen, much as he still loved her, could not make him smile. He attended the many splendid events of the consecration in a quiet, melancholy spirit.

Among the many who had come to witness the consecration and sealing of the peace at St. Denis, was one that few had expected would arrive, so much did he loathe crowds and merrymaking. He had been invited because every important person in the church had been invited. And most of them, including the Pope, had come. But this man who lived a gaunt and ascetic life away from all the pleasures of the world was not one for feasting on wine and mutton. He was Bernard, Abbot of Clairvaux, and when he spoke, men listened. Suger listened; the Pope listened; and the King listened.

So great was his ability to persuade that, when he made his sermons, women hid their sons and husbands at home, lest they follow Bernard's call, and enter a monastery. He was so ascetic that those who knew him told of how he tasted no difference between wine and water; days passed as he fasted, eating nothing; and he had once, mistakenly, ridden out on a nobleman's fine horse, not noticing that it was not the little, gray donkey that usually carried him. He was thin and frail, with bright and feverish skin, but when he spoke his voice was that of a strong and potent person, and what he spoke about was sin . . . sin and salvation.

Years earlier, Bernard had urged Suger to rid St. Denis of the bad habits its monks had fallen into under Abbot Adam. They ate what they wished; they read what they wished; they spoke with knights, and kings, and ladies of the court. Suger had done many things to bring a more pious atmosphere back to St. Denis, but for him, unlike Bernard, a monk's life need not be one devoid of all comforts and pleasures. Indeed, in fixing up his church, one of the first things he had done was to replace the old copper and stone choir stalls, where the monks sang, with wooden ones, which were far warmer in cold weather. Under Suger's rule as abbot, the monks ate well, although they did not banquet every night. After dinner, he loved to sit with them,

laughing and talking about the day, reciting poems, and telling stories about the places he had been and the things he had seen. His room at St. Denis was no place of physical punishment like Bernard's cell at Clairvaux; though it was small, it was neat and his cot was covered with bright, gay fabrics in the daytime.

Suger was, more than anything else, a reasonable man; for his time, he was unusually tolerant. He often disagreed with Bernard, not only about the kind of life monks should lead, but about beliefs and the right of people to have their own ideas and to express them. He was always cautious in dealing with Bernard, however. For no one knew better than Suger that Bernard was very close to the Pope, and to make an enemy of the ascetic abbot was disastrous.

Suger must have wondered what Bernard would think of his church, for he had thundered out so often against the beauties of the world, as temptations of the Devil. But for Suger, there was no way the human imagination could envision the things of Heaven, except through the beauty to be found on earth. He believed that in the enjoyment of beauty, men could rise higher, and turn that love of beauty into love of good.

Bernard seems to have said nothing about the glowing windows, the soaring arches, the jeweled altar, and the great bronze doors. He did, however, after this trip to St. Denis, write a fierce diatribe against the ladies of the court, painted and dressed in silks, smiling flirtatiously, and laden down with jewels. So perhaps he had noticed the beautiful young Queen Eleanor, as he studied her husband, the war-making King Louis. For it was evidently to see Louis that he had come. He engaged the King in conversation as often as he could.

If Bernard had expected a fierce and arrogant warrior, he must have been pleasantly surprised by the monkish king. Louis, himself, seems to have welcomed the chance to talk with Bernard and begged him for an answer to the sickness that had taken his soul. He told Bernard that not even prayers could make him for-

get the fire at Vitry, or enable him to live with himself. After Bernard talked long with the young King, he seemed happier.

Whether it was Bernard's counsel, or his own decision, no one knows, but after the consecration was over, Louis declared that he had decided to do something that might bring him the salvation he feared he had lost forever. He was going to make a Crusade. The Holy Land still was not free, and he felt it was his duty and his privilege to lead an army of pious warriors into Jerusalem, drive the Caliph out, and make it a Christian land. This, and only this, seemed certain, as far as he was concerned, to silence the cries of the dying people of Vitry. Whether or not this was Bernard's idea, it was soon apparent that he approved. He and others applauded the young King's decision.

CHAPTER SEVEN

uger was horrified. Had all his work, all his care over the years, to create a King of France come to this? The King was needed at home to repair the damage done by the long war with Thibault. But instead he was going off, abandoning his country, and the Queen was planning to accompany him. Suger tried to persuade Louis to stay at home, but no argument would work. Suger had always gotten on well with the high-spirited Eleanor, and he turned to her for help. But, she too, was determined to go on what seemed a wonderful adventure.

Eleanor had long been bored with the staid and gloomy French court. Often she had said to Suger that she had thought to marry a King, but found instead she had married a monk. She had even spoken with Suger about a divorce. But Suger, knowing how much the French crown needed the rich lands that were part of Eleanor's dowry, managed to convince her otherwise. And perhaps it was not only land, perhaps Suger still hoped that Eleanor might turn Louis into a king that

France could be proud of. And, of course, Suger was not alone in hoping that she would produce a son to become King after Louis died. As yet, she and Louis had but one child, a daughter, and in the Capet family, the throne could be passed on only to a man.

So Eleanor was no help. And soon all France was excited about the prospects of a Crusade. From town to town Bernard traveled, his passionate voice crying out to all who heard him, to come and join the King on his Crusade to the Holy Land. And not only the people of France heard him; he went to Germany, where although he spoke as a foreigner, people listened, too, and came.

For the first time in his life the Abbot Suger disagreed publicly with the Abbot Bernard. A council to discuss the coming Crusade was called, and at the meeting Suger recounted all the good reasons there were against it. But no one listened. Hopes were high; Bernard was for it; the Pope was for it; the King and Queen were for it; and the Emperor Conrad of Germany had agreed to join it.

And so, as Bernard continued to invite people on the Crusade, Louis and Conrad both began to tax their people to raise the money needed for the enormous undertaking. For nearly three years the money rolled into their treasuries, and more and more volunteers agreed to join them. Suger continued to try to convince Louis and Eleanor that they should not go, but he had little hope of succeeding. And Bernard began to try to convince Suger that he was wrong; he even pointed out that the Crusade, including in its ranks many beggars, paupers, criminals and malcontents, would rid France of many social evils. But Suger remained unconvinced.

In 1147, early in the year, all preparations for the Crusade were complete. In June, however, a celebration was to be held in honor of St. Denis. Louis decided to wait and attend this festival, in order to receive the special blessing of the saint. On June 11, the Pope himself came to St. Denis from Rome and gave Louis a Pilgrim's staff and the crimson Oriflamme to carry into the holy battle.

At the same service, Louis left his crown with Abbot Suger. He named him Regent of France, to govern as king.

Immediately after the festival, Louis and Eleanor set out for Vézelay, in Burgundy, to meet the Abbot Bernard, who would bestow a final blessing on the Crusade. At Vézelay, Bernard addressed the thousands of people who had come to follow Louis. Norman, Burgundian, Breton and Poitevan knights and noblemen were there, as were thousands of foot soldiers, many of them the robbers, murderers, and those who

had been left paupers by the civil war. All received the blessing of Bernard, and some received little white crosses he scattered among them, cut from his own woolen cassock. This done, the pilgrims set out on their journey east to Jerusalem.

Meanwhile in Paris the Abbot Suger turned his eyes to the French kingdom. It was a sad and desolate land with its soldiers and King absent, its treasury empty, its people broken and impoverished by war. It was a kingdom that he must govern alone, with no counsel to guide him.

CHAPTER EIGHT

uger governed well. He devised new and fairer
means of taxation; he passed laws preventing the
wasteful deforestation that he had come to know
too well when he rebuilt St. Denis; and he put
down a revolt in which a group of nobles planned to
overthrow the absent King Louis and make his brother,
Robert, Count of Dreux, King. All the while, letters
from the King begged constantly for more money to
aid in the success of the Crusade.

The Crusade was not going well. Each letter that
Suger received brought news of yet another defeat on
the way to Jerusalem. Attacked by their enemies and
betrayed by their friends, the armies of Louis and Conrad grew smaller each month. Suger had sent a monk
of St. Denis, Odo, as chaplain to the King. Odo re-
ported frankly all that was going on, and the letters he
wrote to Suger were filled with news even more dis-
couraging than those from the King. He told that although the King behaved with great generosity and
kindness to the wounded and seemed always to think

of them before himself, and though he fought bravely in battle, his strategy was without sense or plan. He chose, for example, to linger at Christmas time in a beautiful valley in Turkey, at a place where a river emptied into the sea. Gaily colored tents were pitched and the exhausted horses were let out to pasture. But just as the Christmas services were beginning, the river, swollen with mountain rains, overflowed its banks. With the flood came a strong wind, which swept away the bright tents, while the flood washed horses and donkeys, supplies and men, into the sea. Louis escaped the flood, along with many other Crusaders. But all were seriously impoverished. At this disaster, Conrad had had enough of the erratic plans of the Frankish King and left with what little was left of his army (most had deserted months before) alone for Jerusalem.

Louis followed later. At last he and his army reached the port of Satalia, which was owned by Christian Greeks. They agreed to furnish boats for the Crusaders to cross the sea to Antioch. The boats were welcome, for by this time the army was without shoes or transportation. They had been forced to eat those few horses and donkeys left after the flood in order to avoid starvation. The Crusaders soon discovered, however, that they had been betrayed by the Greeks. The boats furnished were small and unseaworthy. Far worse, the price demanded for transporting each man was too high for Louis to pay; his money was nearly gone. Passage inland over forty miles of wilderness was out of the question; the only way was by sea, and yet, this was impossible. At last, Louis took the only course left to him. He and a few knights and noblemen embarked in the leaky little ships, leaving more than seven thousand foot soldiers behind in Satalia. These hungry men were kept out of the city by the Greeks, who feared robbery by the starving horde. Beyond the outer walls of Satalia, the Mohammedan Turks awaited battle with the men. There was no place of safety for them. Before long, plague broke out, and many died. Those who lived, did the only thing they could, they fled to the open fields where the Turks lay waiting.

On those fields a strange thing happened. The Turks, seeing the miserable condition of the men, took pity on them and brought them into their camp where they fed and clothed them. And as a result of this act of charity, many of Louis' foot soldiers, made up of the rabble of Europe and promised salvation by Bernard of Clairvaux, were saved and converted to Mohammedanism. They were never heard of again.

Nearly a year after he had left St. Denis, in May of 1148, Louis, bearing his pilgrim's staff and the Oriflamme, reached the many-domed city of Jerusalem.

He wept at the sight of it. Then accompanied by the poor remnants of his once-great army, he entered the Holy City. The group was joyously greeted by the Christian community of Jerusalem, and also by Conrad, who had arrived earlier. Together, Conrad and Louis finally went to war against the Mohammedans; but on the field of battle, because of a last minute change in their strategy, they found themselves cut off from water and supplies, and without even an enemy, for the Mohammedans had retreated, leaving the Christians to die of thirst.

They did not die, but instead returned to Jerusalem, all hope of military victory gone. The Second Crusade had come to an end. Suger heard the news first from Odo and wrote the King at once, begging him to come home promptly and govern his kingdom. He told of the enemies he had put down, of the prosperity that was, amazingly, returning to the land, and of the peace that awaited him. But Louis would listen to none of it. His piety overcame what little common sense he had, and he decided to spend a year in Jerusalem in order to celebrate the entire Christian calendar in its churches!

Implore as he did, Suger could not make the King return. And so, he went on ruling alone as Regent of France for yet another year. Meanwhile, from Odo and from the King himself, he heard more bad news.

The marital problems of the King and Queen had grown far worse. Eleanor, disgusted by the disasters of the Crusades, for which she blamed the King, was pressing even harder for a divorce.

All things come to an end, however, and after a year of penance and prayer, in 1149, Louis VII finally said good-bye to Jerusalem and began the long journey back to his throne at Paris.

But even on this journey, bad luck followed him; he reached home only after being shipwrecked in the Mediterranean Sea. Although he never spoke of it, or told the details of what had happened, the accident so upset him that he never set foot in any kind of boat again.

Merrymaking filled the streets of Paris upon the return of the King and Queen. There were those who whispered that having tasted the power of being King, Suger would not return the crown to Louis. But those who said this were mistaken; Suger promptly, and with great modesty, turned his office over to the long absent King. Louis, in one of the few sensible statements he ever made, thanked Suger for his good and wise rule and gave him a new title, which no one in France, before or since, has ever held.

He named him: "Father of his country."

CHAPTER NINE

ith the return of the King, Suger felt free to return to the work he most loved. For a long time he had wanted to remodel the nave of St. Denis, so that it would harmonize with the front and the apse. Now free of his heavy duties, he began to raise the money necessary.

At the same time, he managed to convince the Queen that she should not divorce the King. She had borne him another child since their return, another daughter, and she used this fact as an argument for the divorce. With no son, after more than ten years of marriage, she said, she felt a divorce was wise. But with Suger's counsel, she agreed to wait, and the divorce did not come.

During the two years of the Crusade, Suger had not neglected his monks at St. Denis. He had worshipped with them, guided them, and sat and laughed with them for pleasure and relaxation, many times reliving the happy days when he had been rebuilding St. Denis. When he returned to the monks full time, they reminded him that he was growing old, and that the story of his building should be written down. At the time he was hard at work on a biography of the young King, to be a companion to the volume he had written some years earlier, telling the story of Louis the Fat. But the idea of a book about the church appealed to him, and he began that, too.

While writing the story of the remodeling of the front and apse, his memory was refreshed by a return to meeting with and hiring stone masons, glass workers, and carpenters. This time the work was on the nave. The side walls of the new nave were to be as transparent as the apse was; they would blaze with colored windows down the entire length. The work probably began sometime around 1150.

But the building did not go on for long. For some unknown reason, Suger, wise, sensible, and prudent, decided to lead a third Crusade to Jerusalem. Perhaps he was as depressed as anyone else by the failure of Louis' crusade and could not help but wonder if it would have succeeded if it had been better planned. In any case, whatever his reasons, he began, with the help of Bernard of Clairvaux, to plan and raise money for a Crusade, to be led by the two of them.

Bernard, although he was a younger man than Suger, was very frail from years of fasting. Before the journey could begin, he reluctantly decided that he dare not go. And so, although he was nearly seventy years old, Suger revised his plans, and began to organize a Crusade that he alone would lead.

Fortunately, perhaps, his plans were not to bear fruit. In the winter of 1151, he fell ill with malaria. As Christmas drew near, he saw that he would not live much longer. Knowing that the death of their abbot would cause the monks to go into mourning, Suger prayed that death would wait until after the gay holiday season, so as not to spoil it for the monks. His prayers were granted; he died just after the year turned and the holidays came to an end. His new nave was just begun, and his Crusade was never made.

The stone masons who had worked on St. Denis moved on and taught their work to others. And at the new cathedrals of Sens and Chartres, begun not long after St. Denis, the same pointed arches, rib-vaulted walls and stained glass windows were built. We call this style Gothic. It became the model for how a church should look, so much so, that it is difficult for us to understand how strange and marvelous the early church at St. Denis appeared to the people who first saw it. It seemed to people of the 12th Century that this style, with its transparent walls that seemed to dissolve

into light, and soaring stones that seemed to defy their own weight, expressed the restless, soaring spirituality that led them through the world on pilgrimages and crusades, searching for nothing less than the meaning of life.

And yet, the man who appears to have been the inventor of the style, which so transcends the cares and troubles of the world, was a man who, more than most, lived in the world and was very much a part of all of its troubles. He loved life; and yet his biographer, a monk of St. Denis, tells us that when Suger died he left life in dignity and not as one who is thrown out against his will.

After Suger died, Eleanor obtained her divorce. She promptly married Henry Plantagenet, Count of Anjou, who soon became Henry II of England. By this marriage, the rich lands of Poitou and Acquitaine became, for many years, a possession of the English crown.

In 1154, Bernard of Clairvaux, completely wasted by his fasts, died. Today we call him by the title he received in 1174, St. Bernard.

Louis married again and ruled on, grown somewhat wiser. Throughout his land during the time of his rule, the great Gothic cathedrals were begun, inspired by the beginning made at St. Denis. Even in England, when the choir of Canterbury Cathedral had burned down and needed rebuilding, it was to France that the English turned. They called in a French architect, William of Sens, and asked him to build them a cathedral as glorious as those of France. This he did and in this way the style went from land to land, a French style that seemed to speak to every man, wherever he lived, in those strange and wonder-filled times.

EPILOGUE

n the mouldy stones of St. Denis lies written the history of France.

In the next century after Suger's, the nave was rebuilt in the high Gothic style of the thirteenth century. The man who directed its rebuilding was one Suger would have admired, for he succeeded in being, at the same time, both King and saint. This man was Louis IX, or St. Louis.

From the time of St. Louis on, the church was the royal abbey of France. The Oriflamme rested upon its altar, to be presented to the French king when he went out to battle, and many kings of France were crowned and buried there.

But by the eighteenth century, the monarchy in France had decayed; the monarchs had lost touch with the needs of their people. To many the Kings seemed a greedy luxury that the nation could no longer afford. In 1789 the French Revolution began. Later the King and Queen were guillotined. Angry mobs, embittered by the self-indulgence of royalty, swept into St. Denis and scattered the bones and ashes of the Kings who lay buried there. Most of the lovely stained glass windows were broken with rocks, and the tall, slender jamb figures, standing at the entrances of Suger's triple doors, were thrown to the ground, their smiling, tranquil heads left to roll down the muddy gutters of revolutionary Paris.

Today, a subway and bus ride from the heart of Paris, in a dreary, dingy quarter of the city, the ancient abbey church still stands, a pathetic wreck of its once lovely self. But enough of a ghost remains to tell us of the greatness it once knew, and the beauty it was. The abbey, with its vast lands and wonderful library, is no more. The Abbot Suger would not recognize his masterpiece, should he be able to see it. Yet it and the other Gothic structures it inspired are still a witness and expression of a time long ago. The story of St. Denis tells us something of the people of that time, of what they did and why.